# Classics *for* Young Readers

Editor: John Holdren

Art Director: Steve Godwin

Designer: Elena López

Language Arts Advisor: Michele Josselyn

Illustrators:
Scott Brooks
Vince McGinley
Deborah Wolfe Ltd: (Jerry Dadds, Nancy Harrison, Jim Hays, Richard Hoit, Kelly Hume, Jeff LeVan, Richard Waldrep)

ISBN: 1-931728-00-3

# TABLE OF CONTENTS

# THE LITTLE RED HEN

A little red hen once found a grain of wheat. "Who will help me plant this wheat?" she asked.

"I won't," said the dog.

"I won't," said the cat.

"I won't," said the pig.

"I won't," said the turkey.

"Then I will," said the little red hen. So she planted the grain of wheat.

Soon the wheat began to grow. By and by it grew tall and ripe. "Who will help me cut this wheat?" asked the little red hen.

"I won't," said the dog.

"I won't," said the cat.

"I won't," said the pig.

"I won't," said the turkey.

"I will, then," said the little red hen. So she cut the wheat.

"Who will take this wheat to the mill to have it ground into flour?" asked the little red hen.

"I won't," said the dog.

"I won't," said the cat.

"I won't," said the pig.

"I won't," said the turkey.

"I will, then," said the little red hen. So she took the wheat to the mill.

By and by she came back with the flour. "Who will help me bake a loaf of bread with this flour?" asked the little red hen.

"I won't," said the dog, the cat, the pig, and the turkey.

"I will, then," said the little red hen. So she baked a loaf of bread with the flour.

"Who will help me eat this bread?" asked the little red hen.

"I will!" said the dog.

"I will!" said the cat.

"I will!" said the pig.

"I will!" said the turkey.

"No, you won't," said the little red hen. "My little chicks and I are going to do that." So she called her four little chicks, and they ate the loaf of bread.

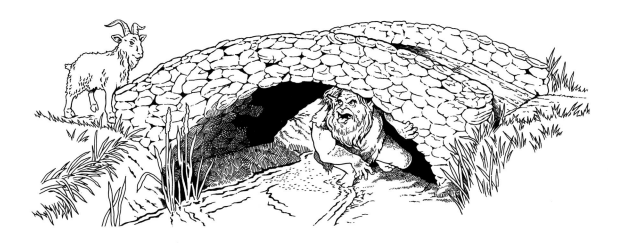

# THREE BILLY GOATS GRUFF

Once there were three billy goats. They were all named "Gruff."

Every day they went up a hill to eat the grass and grow fat. They had to go over a little brook before they came to the hill.

Over the brook was a bridge. A Troll lived under the bridge. He was so big and mean that everyone was afraid of him.

One day the three billy goats were going up the hill to get fat. Little Billy Goat Gruff was the first to cross the bridge.

Trip-trap! Trip-Trap! went the bridge.

"Who is that tripping on my bridge?" called the Troll.

"Oh, it is just Little Billy Goat Gruff. I am going up the hill to get fat," said the little billy goat.

"Well, I am coming to gobble you up!" said the Troll.

"Oh, no!" said Little Billy Goat. "Do not take me! I am too little. Wait for Second Billy Goat. He is bigger than I am."

"Well, be off with you!" said the Troll.

Soon Second Billy Goat Gruff came to the bridge.

*Trip-trap! Trip-Trap! Trip-Trap!* went the bridge.

"Who is that tripping on my bridge?" called the Troll.

"Oh, it is just Second Billy Goat Gruff. I am going up the hill to get fat," said the second billy goat.

"Well, I am coming to gobble you up!" said the Troll.

"Oh, no!" said Second Billy Goat. "Do not take me. I am not very big. Wait for Big Billy Goat. He is bigger than I am."

"Well, be off with you!" said the Troll.

Just then Big Billy Goat Gruff came to the bridge. TRIP-TRAP! TRIP-TRAP! TRIP-TRAP! TRIP-TRAP! went the bridge.

"Who is that tripping on my bridge?" called the Troll.

"Oh, it is just Big Billy Goat Gruff! I am going up the hill to get fat."

"Well, I am coming to gobble you up!" said the Troll.

"Come along, then, Troll!" said Big Billy Goat Gruff.

So the Troll came along. Big Billy Goat Gruff flew at him. He caught the Troll on his horns and threw him into the brook.

The Troll was frightened. He jumped out of the water and ran away.

The three billy goats never saw him again. They go up the hill every day, and now they are as fat as they can be.

# OLD MOTHER HUBBARD

Old Mother Hubbard
Went to the cupboard,
To get her poor dog a bone;
But when she came there,
The cupboard was bare,
And so the poor dog had none.

She took a clean dish
To get him some tripe;
But when she came back,
He was smoking a pipe.

She went to the hatter's
To buy him a hat;
But when she came back,
He was feeding the cat.

She went to the barber's
To buy him a wig;
But when she came back,
He was dancing a jig.

She went to the tailor's
To buy him a coat;
But when she came back,
He was riding a goat.

She went to the cobbler's
To buy him some shoes;
But when she came back,
He was reading the news.

This wonderful dog
Was Dame Hubbard's delight;
He could sing, he could dance,
He could read, he could write.

# THE GINGERBREAD MAN

One day an old woman was making gingerbread cookies. Her little boy was looking on. She made a Gingerbread Man for him.

She put sugar on the head for hair. She put in two raisins for eyes. Then she went out to call the old man to his dinner.

She said to her little boy, "Stay here and watch the oven. See that the cookies do not burn. And watch the Gingerbread Man. We do not know what he may do."

Well, the boy watched the oven for a time. But, by and by he went out to get a drink of water.

As soon as he was out of the door, the Gingerbread Man hopped out of the pan, jumped out of the oven, and was down on the floor. The boy heard him and ran back as fast as he could. He tried to shut the door. But he was not in time.

In a minute the Gingerbread Man was through the door and out in the yard. He ran through the yard. He ran out into the road, and he kept running as fast as he could go.

The boy ran after him. He called to his mother. The old woman saw what had happened, and she ran too. The old man saw them, and he ran as fast as he could.

But they could not run fast enough. They could not catch the Gingerbread Man. So they walked back home.

The Gingerbread Man ran on and on. By and by he came to two farmers. "Wait a minute," they cried. "You look good enough to eat. Come here, and we will eat you." But the Gingerbread Man did not stop.

He ran and called out:

> "Run, run, as fast as you can.
> You can't catch me,
> I'm the Gingerbread Man!
> I've outrun a woman,
> A boy, and a man.
> I can outrun you,
> I'm sure that I can."

Down the road he ran. The farmers ran behind him as fast as they could. But they could not catch him. So they walked back home.

The Gingerbread Man ran on and on. He came to two puppies by the road. First they saw him, and then they smelled him. He smelled good enough to eat.

"Wait a minute," they said. "You smell good enough to eat. Wait, so that we can eat you." But the Gingerbread Man ran on. He called back:

> "Run, run, as fast as you can.
> You can't catch me,
> I'm the Gingerbread Man!
> I've outrun two farmers,
> As fast as they ran,

A little old woman,

A boy, and a man.

I can outrun you, too,

I'm sure that I can."

Down the road ran the Gingerbread Man. The puppies ran after him. They ran as fast as they could. They ran until their legs were tired. But they could not run fast enough to catch the Gingerbread Man. So they walked back home.

The Gingerbread Man ran on and on. By and by he came to a fox. The fox was lying close by the road. He did not move. He called to the Gingerbread Man, "Good morning. You seem to be in a hurry. Where are you going so fast?" The Gingerbread Man stopped a minute.

He wanted to hear what the fox said. "You are a fine runner," said the fox. "Where are you going so fast?"

Then the Gingerbread Man said:

"Run, run, as fast as you can.
You can't catch me,
I'm the Gingerbread Man!
I've outrun the puppies,
And farmers who ran,
A little old woman,
A boy, and a man.
I can outrun you, too,
I'm sure that I can."

"Oh," said the fox, "I see. It's those fine legs of yours. I think I never saw such fine legs. Please come closer. Let me see those fine legs. Don't be in such a hurry."

The Gingerbread Man came closer.

"Do come closer," said the fox. "You are so fast. I'm sure I can't outrun you."

The Gingerbread Man came closer to the fox. Then the fox gave one jump and one bite with his teeth.

And that was the end of the Gingerbread Man!

# OVER IN THE MEADOW

Over in the meadow,
In the sand, in the sun,
Lived an old mother toad
And her little toadie one.
"Wink!" said the mother;
"I wink," said the one.
So she winked and she blinked
In the sand, in the sun.

Over in the meadow,
Where the stream runs blue,
Lived an old mother fish
And her little fishes two.
"Swim!" said the mother;
"We swim," said the two.
So they swam and they leaped
Where the stream runs blue.

Over in the meadow,
In a hole in a tree,
Lived a mother bluebird
And her little bluebirds three.
"Sing!" said the mother;
"We sing," said the three.
So they sang and were glad
In the hole in the tree.

Over in the meadow,
In the reeds on the shore,
Lived a mother muskrat
And her little muskrats four.
"Dive!" said the mother;
"We dive," said the four.
So they dived and they burrowed
In the reeds on the shore.

Over in the meadow,
In the snug beehive,
Lived a mother honeybee
And her little honeys five.
"Buzz!" said the mother;
"We buzz," said the five.
So they buzzed and they hummed
In the snug beehive.

*Olive A. Wadsworth*

# THE COUNTRY MOUSE AND THE CITY MOUSE

Once there was a mouse. She lived in the country.

One day her cousin came to see her. Her cousin lived in the city.

The Country Mouse was very glad to see the City Mouse and asked her to stay to dinner. "Thank you," said the City Mouse. And she took off her hat and coat, and helped to put the dishes on the table.

When dinner was ready, the City Mouse looked at the corn and the beans, and said to herself, "What a funny dinner! Not a bit of cake or cheese.

"Come to my house," she said. "I have cheese every day for my dinner."

"Thank you very much," said the Country Mouse. "I'll go."

So the two mice went to the city. When they got there, they were very hungry. "Come to the kitchen," said the City Mouse. "I'll show you where the Cook keeps the things."

The City Mouse ran across the kitchen and into a big closet. "The Cook made a pie," she said. "I must find it."

She looked around in the closet until she found the pie. "Here it is," said the City Mouse. "This is better than corn and beans."

Just as they were beginning to eat, they heard a terrible noise in the kitchen. "What's that?" asked the Country Mouse.

"That's the Cat," whispered the City Mouse. "Run!"

Both mice ran. When they were safe, the Country Mouse asked, "Why did you run?"

"Never stay in the kitchen when the Cat comes," said the City Mouse. "She would eat you up. We will go to the cellar and find some apples. I like apples."

So away the two mice went to the nice, cool cellar.

"What a lot of apples!" said the Country Mouse. "And there is a big pot of soup. Do you smell cheese? I do."

"Yes, I smell cheese," said the City Mouse, "but we won't eat it. It is in a trap."

"What is a trap?" asked the Country Mouse.

The City Mouse showed her the trap. "The Cook puts cheese in it," said the City Mouse, "but if you eat the cheese, something comes down hard on your head and kills you."

The Country Mouse looked at the trap. "I will go home," she said. "I do not like your house. There is a cat in the kitchen and a trap in the cellar. I like my corn and beans better than your cake and apples."

# THE THREE BEARS

Once upon a time, there were three bears who lived in a house in the woods. One was a great big Papa Bear, one was a middle-sized Mama Bear, and one was a wee little Baby Bear.

Each bear had a dish for porridge. The great big Papa Bear had a great big dish. The middle-sized Mama Bear had a middle-sized dish. And the wee little Baby Bear had a wee little dish.

Each bear had a chair to sit in and a bed to lie on.

One morning Mama Bear made some nice porridge. So she put it into the porridge dishes. It was too hot to eat. So they all went out for a walk, to give it time to get cool.

They left the door open. While they were gone a little girl named Goldilocks came to the house.

First she looked in at the window. Then she peeped in at the door. She saw no one in the house so she walked in.

She was very glad when she saw the porridge. First she took a taste of the porridge of Papa Bear, but it was too hot.

Then she took a taste of the porridge of Mama Bear, but that was too cold.

Then she took a taste of the porridge of Baby Bear. That was just right, and she liked it so well that she ate it all up.

Then she sat down in the chair of Papa Bear, but that was too hard.

So she sat down in the chair of Mama Bear, but that was too soft.

Then she sat down in the chair of Baby Bear. That was just right. But she sat so hard that the bottom of the chair fell out.

Then Little Goldilocks felt sleepy. So she went upstairs.

First she lay down on the bed of Papa Bear, but it was too tall.

Then she lay down on the bed of Mama Bear, but that was too low.

So she lay down on the bed of Baby Bear, and that was just right. She covered herself up and fell fast asleep.

By this time the Three Bears thought their porridge would be cool, so they came home to breakfast.

Little Goldilocks had left the spoon of Papa Bear in his porridge. "SOMEONE HAS BEEN EATING MY PORRIDGE!" said Papa Bear in his great big voice.

When Mama Bear looked at her dish, she saw that the spoon was in it, too. "Someone has been eating my porridge!" said Mama Bear in her middle-sized voice.

Then Baby Bear looked at his dish, and there was the spoon in it, but the porridge was all gone. *"Someone has been eating my porridge, and has eaten it all up!"* said Baby Bear in his wee little voice.

Then the Three Bears began to look about them. "SOMEONE HAS BEEN SITTING IN MY CHAIR!" said Papa Bear in his great big voice.

"Someone has been sitting in my chair!" said Mama Bear in her middle-sized voice.

*"Someone has been sitting in my chair and has sat the bottom out of it!"* said Baby Bear in his wee little voice.

The Three Bears ran upstairs. "SOMEONE HAS BEEN LYING IN MY BED!" said Papa Bear in his great big voice.

"Someone has been lying in my bed!" said Mama Bear in her middle-sized voice.

Then Baby Bear came to look at his bed. There upon the pillow was little Goldilocks, fast asleep. *"Someone has been lying in my bed–and here she is!"* said Baby Bear in his wee little voice.

Little Goldilocks had heard the great big voice of Papa Bear, but she was fast asleep. She had heard the middle-sized voice of Mama Bear, but it was only like someone speaking in a dream. But when she heard the wee little voice of Baby Bear, she sat up wide awake.

When she saw the Three Bears, she gave a cry. She jumped up and ran down the stairs and out the door.

Before the Three Bears could make up their minds what to do, she ran out the door and into the wood. And that was the last the Three Bears saw of Goldilocks.

# THE THREE LITTLE PIGS

There was once a Mother Pig who had three little pigs. One day Mother Pig said to her three little pigs, "You must all go away and seek your fortune."

"Very well, Mother dear," said the three little pigs. And away they went to seek their fortune.

Very soon the first little pig met a man with some straw. He said, "Please, sir, give me some straw to build a house with."

"Very well, I will give you some."

So the first little pig built his house of straw.

Very soon the Big Bad Wolf came to the first little pig's house. He knocked at the door and said, "Little pig, little pig, let me come in."

"No, no, not by the hair of my chinny, chin, chin."

"Then I'll huff and I'll puff, and I'll blow your house in."

And the wolf huffed and puffed and blew the house into bits of straw. The first little pig ran and ran.

Then the second little pig met a man with some wood. He said, "Please, sir, give me some wood to build a house with."

"Very well, you may have some."

So the second little pig built his house of wood.

Very soon the Big Bad Wolf came to the second little pig's house. He knocked at the door and said, "Little pig, little pig, let me come in."

"No, no, not by the hair of my chinny, chin, chin."

"Then I'll huff and I'll puff, and I'll blow your house in."

So he huffed and he puffed, and he blew the house in. The second little pig ran and ran.

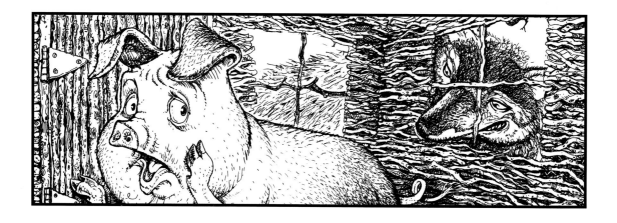

Then the third little pig met a man with some bricks. "Please, sir, give me some bricks to build a house with," he said.

"Very well, you may have some."

So the third little pig built his house of bricks.

Very soon the Big Bad Wolf came to the third little pig's house. He knocked at the door and said, "Little pig, little pig, let me come in."

"No, no, not by the hair of my chinny, chin, chin."

"Then I'll huff and I'll puff, and I'll blow your house in."

So he huffed and he puffed, and he puffed and he huffed, but he could not blow the house in.

Then the Big Bad Wolf said, "Oh, little pig, I know where to get some nice, big, red apples. Be ready tomorrow morning at five o'clock."

"Very well, I will be ready."

But the third little pig got up at four o'clock and went for the apples. He filled his pail with them. Then he went home.

At five o'clock the Big Bad Wolf came. "Are you ready, little pig?" he asked.

"See this pail of nice red apples?" said the third little pig. "I got up at four o'clock and picked them."

This made the Big Bad Wolf very angry, and he growled, *"Grr! Grr!* I am going to eat you, little pig!"

So he climbed up on the roof and went down through the chimney.

The third little pig had a big pot of hot water on the fire. The Big Bad Wolf fell into it. *"Ow! Ow! Ow!"* he yelled. He jumped from the pot and ran out of the house.

The first little pig and the second little pig came to live with their brother in the house of bricks. And they never saw the wolf again.

# THE FOX ON THE HILL

## 1

Once there was a hungry fox.

There were some hungry chickens, too.

The chickens were feeding at the bottom of a hill. The fox was on the top of the hill.

He was looking down. He saw the chickens. The chickens did not see the fox.

The fox said, "I should like a chicken for my dinner. My little ones would like one, too."

Then the fox thought and thought. "How can I get a chicken? If I go down the hill, the chickens will see me. Then they will run away. They will make a great noise, too. Then the dog will come."

And the fox thought and thought and thought.

## 2

When the fox was finished thinking, this is what he did.

He pushed a stone down the hill. It rolled near the chickens. They all ran away. They made a great noise.

The dog came, running and barking, but it did not see the fox. The dog went back to the house.

The chickens went back to their feeding place. They went on eating. They forgot all about the stone.

By and by, the fox pushed another stone down the hill.

The chickens ran away. They made a great noise.

The dog came, running and barking, but it did not see the fox. The dog went back. The chickens came again.

Another stone came down the hill.

The chickens did not turn this time.

They did not mind the stones.

# 3

"Now it is my time!" said the fox. He curled up like a wheel and rolled down the hill.

The chickens thought he was another stone.

The first stone had not hurt them. The second stone had not hurt them. They did not think this stone would hurt them.

They went on feeding.

The fox stopped near them. He kept very still, like a stone.

The chickens were moving about. They were eating in the grass. They did not look at the stone. They did not know that it was the fox.

By and by, the stone began to move. But the chickens were not looking at it.

One chicken came close to the stone.

The stone jumped upon the chicken.

Then the other chickens saw that the stone was a fox. They all ran away. They made a great noise.

The dog came, running and barking. But the fox was gone. The chicken was gone with him.

The little foxes had chicken for dinner.

# THE CAMEL AND THE PIG

One day a camel and a pig were talking. The camel was proud because he was tall. But the pig was proud because he was short.

"Just look at me!" said the camel. "See how tall I am! It is better to be tall, like me."

"Oh, no!" said the pig. "Just look at me! See how short I am! It is better to be short, like me."

"If I am not right, I will give up my hump," said the camel.

"If I am not right, I will give up my snout," said the pig.

Soon they came to a garden. All around it was a wall. There was no gate in the wall.

The camel was so tall that he could see over the wall. He could see fine, ripe fruit in the garden. His neck was so long that he could reach over the wall and get the fruit. He ate all he wanted.

But the poor pig was short. He could not reach over the wall. He could not get inside, because there was no gate.

"Ha, ha, ha!" laughed the camel. "Now would you rather be tall or short?"

Soon they came to another garden. All around it was a high wall. It was so high that the camel could not see over it.

But there was a low gate in the wall. The pig went through the gate.

This garden was full of fine ripe fruit, too. The pig ate all he wanted. But the camel was so tall that he could not get through the low gate.

"Ha, ha, ha!" laughed the pig. "Now would you rather be tall or short?"

So the camel kept his hump, and the pig kept his snout. For they said, "It is sometimes better to be tall, and sometimes better to be small."

# THE CROW AND THE PITCHER

A thirsty crow flew to a pitcher that had a little water in it.

He could not reach the water with his beak. He tried and he tried and he tried, but he had to give up.

Then a thought came to him. He took a pebble and dropped it into the pitcher.

Then he took another pebble and dropped it into the pitcher.

Then he took another pebble and dropped that into the pitcher.

Then he took another pebble and dropped that in.

Then he took another and dropped that in.

After a while, he saw the water begin to rise. So he put in some more pebbles. Then he was able to drink.

# THE FOX AND THE CRANE

One morning a sly fox met a crane. "Come home to dinner with me today," said the fox. "I have something good to eat."

"I shall be very glad to come," said the crane.

So the crane went home with the fox.

The sly fox had soup for dinner, and the soup was in a flat dish.

The crane was a very tall bird. He had a long neck and a long bill, so he could not drink from a flat dish. He tried to eat some soup, but he could not get it into his bill.

He tried and tried, but he could not get any soup. He could not get even a taste of it. The sly fox ate all the soup, and the crane had nothing.

"Your soup smells good," said the crane. The sly fox laughed and laughed. "I am glad you like it," he said. Then the crane flew away home.

One day the crane met the sly fox in the fields. "When are you coming to see me?" asked the crane. "Will you come to supper tonight?"

"I shall be glad to come," said the fox.

So the sly fox went to see the crane.

The crane had soup for supper. It was in a tall pitcher.

"I know you like soup," said the crane. The fox tried to eat the soup, but he could not reach it. He could not reach down the long neck of the pitcher.

Then the crane put his long bill into the pitcher. He ate all the soup he wanted. But the fox could not get even a taste of the soup. He had nothing at all to eat.

"Don't you like this supper?" asked the crane.

"I can not get any of it," said the fox.

"Well, now you see how much I liked *your* dinner," said the crane.

# THE ELVES AND THE SHOEMAKER

## 1

A shoemaker once lived in a little town. He was a good man and worked hard. But he became too poor to buy more leather. At last there was only enough for one pair of shoes. At night he cut out the shoes, but it was too late to make them. He put them on his bench and went to bed with a sad heart.

In the morning he went to finish them. But there they were, all done! Done inside, and done outside!

Now this surprised the good man. It made his eyes grow bigger and bigger. Who in the world could have finished the shoes?

"Wife," he called, "the shoes are done! Come and see."

So she ran to see. Sure enough, there were the shoes all done. Then her eyes grew bigger and bigger. *Who* could have finished the shoes?

While they were wondering, in came a customer. "Have you shoes to sell?" he said.

"One pair, sir," said the shoemaker, and showed the pair on the bench.

"These are very fine shoes," said the customer. "You do not ask enough for them. I will pay you more."

So he paid the shoemaker double the price. Then there was money for more leather, and the shoemaker bought enough for two more pairs of shoes. He cut out the new leather at night.

"I will finish these shoes in the morning," he said. "Come, wife, it is late. Let us go to bed."

Next morning he went to his bench, and there were the two pairs of shoes all finished! He and his wife wondered and wondered. *Who* could have been kind enough to finish the shoes?

While they were wondering, in came two customers. "Have you shoes to sell?" they asked.

"Two pairs, sirs," said the shoemaker, and he showed them the two pairs on the bench.

"Ah, these are fine shoes, indeed," said one customer.

"So they are," said the other. "Let us pay this good man a fair price for them."

So they paid him double the price of the shoes. Then there was more money for leather. This time there was enough for four more pairs of shoes.

## 2

This kept going on. Each night the shoemaker cut out his shoes. Each morning he found them finished. Each day his customers paid him a high price.

At last he began to be rich. But still he did not know who was making his shoes.

One night he called his wife. "Let us sit up tonight," he said. "We can hide behind the door. Then we can see who makes the shoes."

"Good!" said the wife. "Let us do so. I, too, should like to see who helps us."

After the shoes were cut out, the old people hid behind the door and peeped through the crack.

By and by, in ran two little ragged men. They were no bigger than your hand. *Skippety hop!* They ran to the bench. They picked up the shoes. Then, *rappety rap!* How they worked! In no time the shoes were finished. Then, *hoppety skip,* away they went again!

The old people rubbed their eyes to see if it was true. Yes, it was. For there were the shoes all finished.

Next day the shoemaker's wife said, "The little elves have been very kind to us. Let us do something to make them glad. Let us give them some new clothes. I will make the clothes, and you can make some little shoes."

So the good woman sewed all day. She made two little blue suits and several little white shirts. Last of all she knitted two wee pairs of short red stockings.

The shoemaker made two tiny pairs of shoes. At night they put the new things on the bench. Then they hid behind the door again.

The clock struck twelve. In skipped the two little elves. Up they jumped to the shoemaker's bench. But there were no shoes to make. There were the new clothes to put on instead. *Whisk,* went the old clothes off!

And *whisk,* went the new clothes on! Then the little men danced for joy. They danced and skipped from the bench. They skipped and danced over the floor. Then they danced out of the door, singing these words:

> *"Happy little elves are we,*
> *Neatly dressed, as you can see,*
> *No more shoemakers to be."*

No one saw them again, but from that day the shoemaker had good luck. His heart was never sad again. He always had money for leather, and his customers paid him well.

So you must know that good luck will come where the elves have danced. But they never dance where men are bad and lazy.

# SWEET PORRIDGE

Once there was a little girl who lived with her mother. They were very poor. Sometimes they had no supper. Then they went to bed hungry.

One day the little girl went into the woods. She wanted wood for the fire. She was so hungry and sad!

"Oh, I wish I had some sweet porridge!" she said. "I wish I had a pot full for mother and me. We could eat it all up."

Just then she saw an old woman with a little black pot. She said, "Little girl, why are you so sad?"

"I am hungry," said the little girl. "My mother is hungry, too. We have nothing to eat. Oh, I wish we had some sweet porridge for our supper!"

"I will help you," said the old woman. "Take this little black pot. When you want some sweet porridge, you must say, *Little pot, boil!* The little pot will boil and boil and boil. You will have all the sweet porridge you want. When the little pot is full, you must say, *Little pot, stop!* Then the little pot will stop boiling."

The little girl thanked the old woman and ran home with the little black pot. Then she made a fire with the wood and put the little black pot on the fire.

"Little pot, boil!" she said. The little pot boiled and boiled and boiled, until it was full of sweet porridge. Then the little girl said, "Little pot, stop!" The little pot stopped boiling.

She called her mother, and they ate all the sweet porridge they wanted. The little girl told her mother about the old woman. "Now," they said, "we are happy. We shall not be hungry any more."

The next day the little girl went into the woods again. She was gone a long time. "She will be hungry when she comes home," said her mother. "I will boil the sweet porridge."

So she put the little black pot on the fire.
"Little pot, boil!" she said. The little pot boiled and
boiled until it was full of sweet porridge. The mother
wanted the pot to stop boiling. But she forgot
what to say!

The pot boiled and boiled. The porridge boiled over
on to the stove. It ran all over the stove. Then it ran all
over the floor. It flowed into the street. It flowed on and
on and on.

The people all ran out of their houses. "Look!" they
cried. "The sea has turned to porridge! It is flowing over
the world! What shall we do?" No one knew how to
make the little black pot stop boiling.

After a long time the little girl came home. The pot
was boiling and boiling. "Little pot, stop!" said the little
girl. And the little pot stopped.

But for many days after that the street was full of
sweet porridge. And when people wanted to get to the
other side, they had to eat their way across!

# BELLING THE CAT

Once some mice lived in a big house. They ran all over the house. *Patter, patter, patter,* went their feet! The house was full of mice.

A cat lived in the big house, too. He was a big cat. He liked to catch the mice. He caught some every day.

The mice were afraid of him. They said, "What shall we do? This big cat will catch us all. He will eat us up. Oh, what shall we do?"

"I know what to do," said a little mouse. "The cat makes no noise when he walks. We can not hear him. I have a fine plan.

"We must hang a bell on his neck! The bell will make a noise. *Ting-a-ling! Ting-a-ling!* We shall hear the bell. Then we shall know that the cat is coming. We will run away. The cat can not catch us."

"What a fine plan!" said the other mice. "Yes! Yes! The cat must have a bell on his neck! Then he can not catch us."

The mice jumped for joy. The little mouse was very proud. "How wise I am!" he said. "Now we shall be safe."

But Old Gray Mouse laughed. He was wiser than the little mouse.

"Ha, ha!" he laughed. "Ha, ha, ha! That is a fine plan, little mouse. But who will hang the bell on the cat? Will you, little mouse?"

"Oh, no, no! He would eat me up!"

"But someone must put the bell on the cat!"

The little mouse had not thought of that.

He ran away as fast as he could go. He cried, "Squeak! Squeak!" all the way home.

# THE FOX AND THE CROW

A crow stole a piece of cheese and flew with it to a tree.

A hungry fox came by. He saw the cheese and wanted it. He wondered how he could get it.

He began to talk to the crow. "What a beautiful bird you are!" he said. "What glossy feathers you have!"

The crow liked to hear this, so she sat still and listened.

"I know," said the fox, "that you must have a sweet voice. How I wish I could hear you sing!"

The crow was so pleased that she opened her mouth to sing.

The cheese fell to the ground. The fox quickly picked it up and ran off with it.

# THE TORTOISE AND THE HARE

Once there was a hare that lived in a meadow. He liked to hop fast. "Look at me!" he said. "I can hop faster than any animal in the meadow."

A tortoise lived in the meadow, too. One day he was creeping to the river for a swim.

"How slow you are!" said the hare. "You can not hop. You can only creep. Look at me! See how fast I hop!" And the little hare gave a great hop.

"I am slow," said the tortoise. "But I am sure. Would you like to run a race with me?"

"Run a race!" cried the hare. "How foolish that would be! I hop and you creep. How can we run a race?"

"Let us try," said the tortoise. "Let us race to the river. We shall see who gets there first."

"The river is a long way off," said the hare. "But I shall get there before you. Good-bye!"

Off went the hare, *hop! hop! hop!*

Off went the tortoise, *creep, creep, creep.*

Soon the hare was nearly to the river. It was a warm day. "I will rest a little," he said.

So the hare rested and ate some leaves. Then he felt sleepy. "It is very warm," he said. "I will sleep a little. That foolish tortoise is slow. I shall wake up before he creeps here. Then I can hop to the river. I shall get there long before he comes."

So the hare went to sleep. The little tortoise came creeping on. He did not stop to eat. He did not stop to sleep. He went on and on, *creep, creep, creep.* By and by he came to the river.

The hare slept a long time. Then he woke up with a jump. "Dear me! I must hop along," he said. "Where can that slow tortoise be? He is not here yet."

The hare hopped on to the river. But who was there waiting for him? The tortoise!

# THE PRINCESS AND THE PEA

Once upon a time there was a prince. He traveled all over the world to look for a real princess. He went to every king he could find, and to each one he said the same thing. "O King, I am seeking a real princess. If I find one, she shall become my wife and share my kingdom."

"That is very easy," said each king. "Here are my daughters. Each of them is a real princess. Take your choice."

When he saw the king's daughters, the prince was never satisfied. "I fear they are not real princesses," he always said. He went from kingdom to kingdom, until he traveled all around the world. At last he came back home again.

His mother, the queen, found him sitting on the steps of the palace. "Did you find a princess?" she asked.

"I found many of them," he replied. "They always said they were real, but I could not be sure."

That night there was a heavy storm. The wind howled and the rain poured. At the very worst part of the storm, there came a knock at the palace gate.

"Who is there?" asked the guard.

"A princess," said a soft voice. "May I come in? I am very cold."

The guard brought the poor princess to the queen at once. Her hair was dripping with rain, and her gown was torn and muddy. Still, she looked like a real princess. "If only I could be sure!" said the prince.

"I will make sure," said the queen. She went away to prepare a fine bed for the princess. The bed was very high and soft. No queen ever had a more beautiful one. Under the very lowest mattress, the queen placed a tiny pea. Then she brought in the tired princess.

"I hope you will rest well tonight," said the queen.

Next morning, at the breakfast table, the princess was very pale.

"Did you rest well?" asked the queen.

"Not at all," said the poor princess. "There was a great lump in my bed, and I really could not sleep at all."

Then the prince and his mother both laughed for joy.

"Our long search is ended!" they cried. "We have found the real princess."

As for the pea, it was put in a box and laid in a safe place. If it is not lost, it is there still.

*Hans Christian Andersen*

# THE PINE TREE AND ITS NEEDLES

A little pine tree lived in the woods. It had leaves like long green needles. But the little pine tree was not happy.

"I do not like my green needles," it said. "I wish I had beautiful leaves. How happy I should be if I only had gold leaves!"

Night came. Then the Fairy of the Trees walked in the woods. "Little pine tree," she said, "you may have your wish."

In the morning the little pine tree had leaves of gold. "How beautiful I am!" it said. "See how I shine in the sun! Now I am happy!"

Night came. Then a man walked in the woods. He took all the gold leaves and put them into a bag. The little tree had no leaves at all.

"What shall I do?" it said. "I do not want gold leaves again. I wish I had glass leaves. Glass leaves would shine in the sun, too. And no one would take glass leaves."

Night came. The Fairy walked in the woods again. "Little pine tree," she said, "you may have your wish."

In the morning the tree had glass leaves. "How beautiful I am!" it said. "See how I shine in the sun! Now I am happy."

Night came. Then the wind came through the woods. Oh, how it blew! It broke all the beautiful glass leaves.

"What shall I do now?" said the tree. "I do not want glass leaves again. The oak tree has big green leaves. I wish I had big green leaves, too."

Night came. Then the Fairy of the Trees walked in the woods again. "Little pine tree," she said, "you may have your wish."

In the morning the little pine tree had big green leaves. "How beautiful I am!" it said. "Now I am like the other trees. At last I am happy."

Night came. A goat came through the woods. He ate all the big green leaves.

"What shall I do?" said the tree. "A man took my leaves of gold. The wind broke my leaves of glass. A goat ate my big green leaves. I wish I had my long needles again."

Night came. The Fairy walked in the woods again. "Little pine tree," she said, "you may have your wish."

In the morning the little pine tree had its long needles again.

"Now I am happy," said the tree. "I do not want any other leaves. Little pine needles are best for little pine trees."

# THE HUMMINGBIRD AND THE BUTTERFLY

*Hummingbird:* What a beautiful creature you are! What splendid wings you have! Do come with me and be my friend.

*Butterfly:* No, thank you, Mrs. Hummingbird, I cannot be your friend.

*Hummingbird:* Why not?

*Butterfly:* You once made fun of me and said that I was ugly and stupid.

*Hummingbird:* This is impossible. I am sure I never called you stupid or ugly.

*Butterfly:* You may not call me that now, but you made fun of me when I was a caterpillar. You did not know that I would some day be a butterfly. You see, it is best to be kind to everybody, for ugly creatures sometimes become beautiful. So, good-bye. I prefer to find other friends.

# THE STORY OF CHICKEN LITTLE

When Chicken Little was in the woods one day, an acorn fell on her head. She thought that the sky was falling, so she ran to tell the King.

On the way she met Henny Penny. "Where are you going, Chicken Little?" asked Henny Penny.

"The sky is falling, and I am going to tell the King."

"I will go with you, if I may," said Henny Penny. And away they both ran.

Soon they met Cocky Locky. "Where are you going, Henny Penny?" asked Cocky Locky.

"The sky is falling, and I am going with Chicken Little to tell the King."

"I will go with you, if I may," said Cocky Locky. And they all ran down the road.

When they came to the pond they saw Ducky Lucky. "Where are you going, Cocky Locky?" asked Ducky Lucky.

"The sky is falling, and we are going to tell the King."

"I will go with you, if I may," said Ducky Lucky. And away they went.

Next they met Goosey Loosey.

"Where are you going, Ducky Lucky?" asked Goosey Loosey.

"The sky is falling, and we are going to tell the King."

"I will go with you, if I may," said Goosey Loosey. "Let us run fast."

At the top of the hill they met Turkey Lurkey.

"Where are you going, Goosey Loosey?" asked Turkey Lurkey.

"The sky is falling, and we are going to tell the King."

"I will go with you, if I may," said Turkey Lurkey. And they all ran down the hill.

Foxy Loxy heard them coming and ran out to meet them. "Where are you going?" he asked.

"The sky is falling, and we are going to tell the King," they cried.

"Come with me, and I will show you the way," said Foxy Loxy.

So Foxy Loxy led Chicken Little, Henny Penny, Cocky Locky, Ducky Lucky, Goosey Loosey, and Turkey Lurkey across the field and through the woods.

He led them straight into his den, and they never saw the King to tell him that the sky was falling.

# THE LION AND THE MOUSE

*Characters:*

**LION · MOUSE · GOAT · CAMEL · MONKEY**

**SCENE 1: THE LION'S DEN**

*[The lion is asleep. A mouse wakes him up.]*

*Lion:* Who woke me from my sleep? A mouse? I will kill you with one blow of my paw.

*Mouse:* Oh, Mr. Lion, please do not kill me. Spare my life.

*Lion:* Why should I spare your life?

*Mouse:* Some day I may do you a good turn, Mr. Lion.

*Lion:* Ha, ha, ha! You do me a good turn! Who ever heard of such a thing! What can a little mouse ever do for a great big lion? But run along. I will spare your life this time.

*Mouse:* Thank you, Mr. Lion. Thank you very much.

*[The mouse runs away.]*

## SCENE 2: IN THE WOODS

*[The lion is caught in a net. The goat, camel, and monkey walk by.]*

*Lion:* Alas! Here I am, caught in the net that the hunters set for me. I can't break it. If only I had a friend to help me!

*Goat:* Oh, there's the lion caught in the net! He'll never get away.

*Camel:* Well, well! Caught at last! He'll never get away.

*Monkey:* Hee, hee! The lion is caught! The lion is caught!

*Lion:* No one will help me. They all laugh at me.

*Mouse:* Do you need a friend now, Mr. Lion? My sharp teeth will help you.

*[The mouse cuts the rope with her teeth.]*

*Lion:* At last I am free again! Thank you, little friend.

*Mouse:* You spared my life one day, and I am glad to help you now.

*Lion:* You have saved my life today.

*Mouse:* I am not too small to do you a good turn, after all. Even a little mouse may help a great lion.

*Lion:* You are right. I see that little friends may be great friends after all.

# THE LITTLE MOUSE AND THE STRANGERS

*Little Mouse:* Squeak! Squeak! Squeak! Oh, Mother, Mother! I have had such a fright!

*Mother Mouse:* What has happened, Little Mouse? Where have you been?

*Little Mouse:* Oh, Mother! I was tired of our little home, so I have been out to see the world.

*Mother Mouse:* Oh, my dear child! Did you go all alone? No wonder you are frightened. Home is best for Little Mouse. Where did you go?

*Little Mouse:* I went to the barnyard. Squeak! Squeak! It frightens me yet, when I think of it.

*Mother Mouse:* Tell me about it. What did you see to frighten you so?

*Little Mouse:* At first I was not frightened. I saw a beautiful animal who looked a little like me.

*Mother Mouse:* A little like you? Oh, no! There is no one like you in the barnyard.

*Little Mouse:* Yes, she was like me, Mother, but she was much bigger than I am. She had fur like mine, but it was much longer.

*Mother Mouse:* Little Mouse, you frighten me. Quick, quick! Tell me more about this animal. I am afraid I know who it was.

*Little Mouse:* She was lying on the grass, in the sun. She looked kind and gentle. I thought she might like little mice, so I started to go up and speak to her. She made a pleasant sound—*purr-r, purr-r, purr-r!*

*Mother Mouse:* Oh, my dear Little Mouse, that was a cat! You have been in great danger. The cat does like little mice, but she likes them to eat! Quick, tell me! You did not try to speak to her, did you?

*Little Mouse:* No, Mother; I did not have time. For just then I saw a strange and dreadful animal.

*Mother Mouse:* Who could that be, Little Mouse? The cat is the most dreadful animal you could see.

*Little Mouse:* Oh, no, Mother! Listen, and I will tell you. This animal had a long, sharp nose.

*Mother Mouse:* A long sharp nose? The pig has a long nose, but it is not sharp.

*Little Mouse:* He had a red chin that shook when he moved.

*Mother Mouse:* A red chin? None of the animals in the barnyard has a red chin. This must have been a strange, wild beast. Tell me more about him.

*Little Mouse:* He had something red on his head, too, and he had only two legs. He stretched out his long neck and made a dreadful noise—*Cock-a-doodle-doo! Cock-a-doodle-doo!*

*Mother Mouse:* Oh, squee-hee-hee! Never mind if I laugh, Little Mouse. Now I know what that strange beast was. That was a rooster! He has a red comb and a long beak, but he will not harm you.

*Little Mouse:* But, Mother, how shall I tell what beasts will harm me? The cat looked so kind, and the rooster looked so fierce.

*Mother Mouse:* Do not speak to strange beasts. You can not tell by their looks what they will do. Remember, Little Mouse, that good deeds are better than good looks.

# Classics for Young Readers, Volume 1
## Text Sources

Selections in this volume have been adapted from the following sources:

*Child Life in Tale and Fable, A Second Reader,* Etta Austin Blaisdell and Mary Frances Blaisdell (New York: The Macmillan Company, 1908)

*The Elson Readers, Book One,* William H. Elson and Lura E. Runkel (Chicago: Scott, Foresman and Company, 1920)

*Everyday Classics, First Reader,* Fannie Wyche Dunn, Franklin T. Baker, and Ashley H. Thorndike (New York: The Macmillan Company, 1924)

*Everyday Classics, Second Reader,* Franklin T. Baker, Ashley H. Thorndike, and Mildred Batchelder (New York: The Macmillan Company, 1922)

*The Merrill Readers, First Reader,* Franklin B. Dyer and Mary J. Brady (New York: Charles E. Merrill Company, 1915)

*The Natural Method Readers, A First Reader,* Hannah T. McManus and John H. Haaren (New York: Charles Scribner's Sons, 1914)

*The Progressive Road to Reading, Book One,* Georgine Burchill, William L. Ettinger, and Edgar Dubs Shimar (New York: Silver, Burdett and Company, 1920)

*Story Hour Readers, First Year-Second Half,* Ida Coe and Alice J. Christie (New York: American Book Company, 1913)

*Story Hour Readers Revised, Book Two,* Ida Coe and Alice C. Dillon (New York: American Book Company, 1914)